I am Preparing for
My First Communion

"Today I want to come and stay at your home"

Original text
Marie-Paule Mordefroid
with Catechist Team

English translation by
John McCollough
Jean-Claude Selvini

Illustrations
Christelle Fargue

GW00854974

McCRIMMONS

God our Father,
you love me and you gave me life

I thank You Lord,
for the love that You
put into the hearts of
Mummy and Daddy

I was born on ...19th...............
...October... 2012

Mummy and Daddy called me
Cristina
Alexzandra Mills

Thank You Lord,
you made me in Your likeness
and image:

You are Love
and I can love also.

Lord,
I want to love You
and to love all those
around me.

I was baptised

"In the name of the Father
and of the Son
and of the Holy Spirit"

on ....

On that day
I became a child of God the Father
a brother/sister of Jesus and
a temple – a dwelling-place, a
home of the Holy Spirit.

I became a member of the huge family
of the children of God – the Church.
And with all Christians I can say:

Our Father, who art in heaven,
hallowed be thy name;
Thy kingdom come;
Thy will be done
on earth as it is in heaven.
Give us this day our daily bread;
and forgive us our trespasses
as we forgive those who trespass
*   against us;*
and lead us not into temptation,
but deliver us from evil.

"Today I want to come and stay at your home"

One day, Jesus spoke those words to a man called Zacchaeus.

You can read about what happened to Zacchaeus in the 19th Chapter of St. Luke's Gospel.

But today you hear those words of Jesus.

Like Zacchaeus you want to know
Jesus better – you want
to become His friend, and above
everything else, you want to receive
Him into your heart.

Receiving Holy Communion
is to receive Jesus into your heart and
soul just as Zacchaeus received Jesus
into his home. For we believe that
Jesus is truly present in the Host – the
Blessed Sacrament.

Write a prayer to the Lord Jesus,
telling Him how much you wish to receive
Him in Holy Communion:

Jesus, the Son of God, came into the world to make known God's love and to save all people

Today a Saviour is born who is called Christ the Lord (Luke 2:11)

Jesus grew and became strong and filled with wisdom.
(Luke 2:40)

Jesus went out to the mountain to pray
(Luke 6:12)

Jesus said "I order you: get up and walk."
(Luke 5:24)

"I am the Bread of Life"

Jesus fed a great crowd of people
with five loaves and two fish.

*"Jesus took the bread, gave thanks to
God and distributed them to all present.
He did the same with the fish.
They had as much as they wanted"*
(John 6:11)

But Jesus
explained to those around Him that they
should not simply look for food for their bodies
but food for their souls – a food which gives
them eternal life.

Jesus said:
*"I am the Bread of Life;
if anyone eats This Bread – he will live forever.
Whoever eats my flesh and drinks my blood has eternal life.
For my flesh is real food and my blood is real drink.
Whoever eats my flesh and drinks my blood lives in me and I live in him"*
(John 6:34-58)

On Holy Thursday

Jesus, knowing that He was about to die,
joined His apostles for a last meal together.
He took some bread, thanked God His Father, and said:

*"Take this, all of you, and eat from it, for this is my Body,
which will be given up for you."*

Then He took a cup of wine and said:

*"Take this all of you, and drink from it,
for this is the chalice of my Blood,
the Blood of the new and eternal covenant,
which will be poured out for you and for many
for the forgiveness of sins.
Do this in memory
of me."*

On Good Friday

Jesus died on the cross
In this offering of His life to God,
He gave us His life also – He is
the Bread of Life.

The Morning of Easter Day

Jesus is risen from the dead – alive.
He comes out of the tomb;
He is alive for evermore.

Alleluia!

Every Sunday

Christians gladly reply to the Lord's invitation – they come together at church for the Mass

Every Sunday we celebrate the Resurrection of Jesus.
It is Jesus who brings us together as one big family.

We praise God our Father.
We ask forgiveness for our sins.
We listen to the Word of God in the scriptures.
We share that meal in which Jesus gives Himself to be our food.

The we go out and meet others and share the Love of Jesus with them.

The church building where Christians meet together is a 'picture' or 'image' of the Church of Jesus the great family of Christians throughout the world, united by Jesus.

The Church of Jesus is like an invisible building; every baptised person is a 'living stone'.

We are the living stones of the Church of Jesus Christ

We ask forgiveness from God

At the beginning of the Mass, we own up to the fact that we are sinners – we know that our hearts are not ready to listen to and receive Jesus. We want to live as Jesus has asked us to live, we want to be His friend, but it is not always easy.

That is why we ask God to forgive us for not having always loved Him, for not having always loved those with whom we live.

We say together:

"I confess to almighty God
and to you, my brothers and sisters,
that I have greatly sinned…"

Then the priest says this prayer:

"May almighty God have mercy on us,
forgive us our sins,
and bring us to everlasting life."

Amen.

I am Preparing for
My First Communion

The time of preparation for a child's First Holy Communion is very special and an important step in the child's life as a Christian. Parents, who are the first teachers of their child, should provide the basis on which he can build a real relationship with God, appreciating the gifts that God gives. Inevitably each child's ability to do this will be different. Prayer, listening to and reading the Word of God in the Scriptures, an openness to the love of God and the desire to live in that love are all ideas which parents should do their utmost to foster. Parents contribute to the growth and strengthening of the life of God that the child received at Baptism. The child also needs the prayers of all the family at this important time.

You will find in this pull-out section
- some important points concerning First Holy Communion (p.iii)
- a short commentary on each of the pages of the booklet (pp.iv & v)
- advice on how to use the booklet (p.vi)
- a 'mountain' diagram which explains how the Mass proceeds (pp.ii & vii)
- some ideas as to how to use the 'mountain' scheme (p.viii)

...ing the
...ead and priest blesses
...ne to the the bread
...est. and wine.

which
becoms
the body
and blood
of christ.

we pray
after
communium

reseving
holy communion.

Jesus
sends us
out.

Use of the 'Mountain scheme'

The 'Mountain scheme' is devised to show how the Mass develops and unfurls and it shows the powerful aspect of what takes place during the Mass.

It shows the way we take, with different points along that way, to ascend to the summit of the mountain where we encounter the crucified and risen Christ in Holy Communion and then descend in order to carry Christ out into the world.

Certain suggestions are made which are developed in the booklet but others can be added.

The principal moments of the Mass can be written on labels (by yourself or by the child) and then stuck onto the mountain diagram at the appropriate point:
- Jesus calls us together (the priest welcomes us)
- We ask the forgiveness of God
- We praise God our Father
- We listen to the Word of God
- We bring the Bread and Wine to the priest who offers them to God
- Repeating the words of Jesus, the priest consecrates the Bread and Wine which become the Body and Blood of Jesus
- In receiving Holy Communion – we receive Jesus
- Jesus sends us out (the priest blesses us)
- We take Jesus with us out into the world

You can also add prayers (the opening words)
- I confess to Almighty God
- Glory to God
- We believe
- Holy, Holy, Holy Lord
- Our Father
- Lamb of God

We praise God our Father

During the Mass we often praise God in what we sing and in what we pray.

• **We sing the Glory of God:**

    "Glory to God in the highest"
    "Holy! Holy! Holy Lord! God of power and might"

• **We praise God:**

    for His word which enlightens us,
    for the death and resurrection of Jesus which has saved us.

• **We thank God:**

    for the Body of Jesus that we receive in Holy Communion

Write here some words of a hymn or a prayer of praise that you especially like:

We listen to The Word of God

Jesus brings us together because He has something to say to us.
He wants to speak to us – to you and to all those who are present.

Jesus loved to talk to His apostles and to the crowds who came to listen to Him.
Today, when the priest reads the Gospel, it is Jesus who is speaking to us.

Jesus says:
"Blessed are those who listen to my words and put them into practice." (Luke 11:28)
That is to say, if you do what He asks of you, you will be truly happy and you will show
Him that you love Him. Therefore, listen carefully to the words of the Gospel.

To prepare carefully to listen to the Word of God, it is a good idea to ask your parents to
read the Gospel of the Sunday Mass to you – or read it yourself – <u>before</u> you go to Mass.

Lord Jesus
Your Word is Light
Your Word is Truth
Your Word is Love
Your Word is Alive

Alleluia!

Write down some words of Jesus that you especially like:

*The Gospel
of the Lord!*

*Praise to You
Lord Jesus Christ!*

15

We take the bread and wine to the Priest who then offers them to God

In doing this, we are offering our lives to God.
At this moment of the Mass you can say to God:
"Lord, I offer you all the joys and all the sadness, all the games I have played,
all the work I have done and all I have tried to do during this past week.

The bread and the wine which the priest offers to God are both a gift from God and the work of Man.
God gives us wheat and the vines and man makes bread from flour which is made from grains of wheat and wine from the grapes which come from the vine.

In our everyday lives it's the same thing. God gives us gifts and we use those gifts that He has given us and then we can offer them back to God.

Blessed are you, Lord God of all creation, for through Your goodness we have received the bread we offer you: fruit of the earth and work of human hands, it will become for us the Bread of Life.

Blessed be God for ever!

17

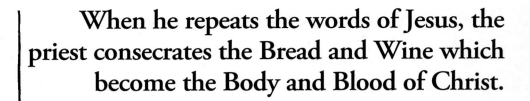

When he repeats the words of Jesus, the priest consecrates the Bread and Wine which become the Body and Blood of Christ.

In the middle of the Mass you hear a very long prayer which is said by the priest(s) alone. During this prayer the priest, representing Jesus, offers to God the Father, the Sacrifice of Jesus Christ. This Sacrifice is the Death and Resurrection of Jesus.

It is for that reason the priest repeats over the bread the words of Jesus at the Last Supper:
"Take this all of you and eat of it, for this is my Body, which will be given up for you."

Then over the cup of wine:
"Take this, all of you, and drink from it, for this is the chalice of my Blood, the Blood of the new and eternal covenant, which will be poured out for you and for many for the forgiveness of sins. Do this in memory of me."

At this moment, through the power and work of God the Holy Spirit, the bread and wine become the Body and Blood of Jesus, crucified and raised from the dead. At this moment you can look upon the Lord Jesus with all your love and say with Saint Thomas:
"My Lord and my God" (John 20:28)

The Mystery of Faith

We proclaim your death, O Lord,
and profess your Resurrection
until you come again.

or

When we eat this Bread and drink this Cup,
we proclaim your Death, O Lord,
until you come again.

or

Save us Saviour of the world,
for by your Cross and Resurrection,
you have set us free.

In receiving Holy Communion, we receive Jesus

Finally there comes the moment when, with all those who are receiving Holy Communion, you can receive our Lord Jesus present in the Sacred Host.

The priest shows us the Body of Christ and says:

> *"Behold the Lamb of God,*
> *behold him who takes away the sins of the world.*
> *Blessed are those called to the supper of the Lamb."*

We reply:

> *"Lord, I am not worthy*
> *that you should enter under my roof,*
> *but only say the word*
> *and my soul shall be healed."*

It is true that we are never sufficiently ready to receive Jesus into our hearts and souls. Our 'homes' will never be sufficiently clean and tidy to receive Jesus, God the Son.

But God loves us so much that he still gives us this great gift – to be able to receive the Lord Jesus in the Blessed Sacrament in Holy Communion.

The Body of Christ.

Amen.

I received Holy Communion for the first time on:

....

In the church of:

....

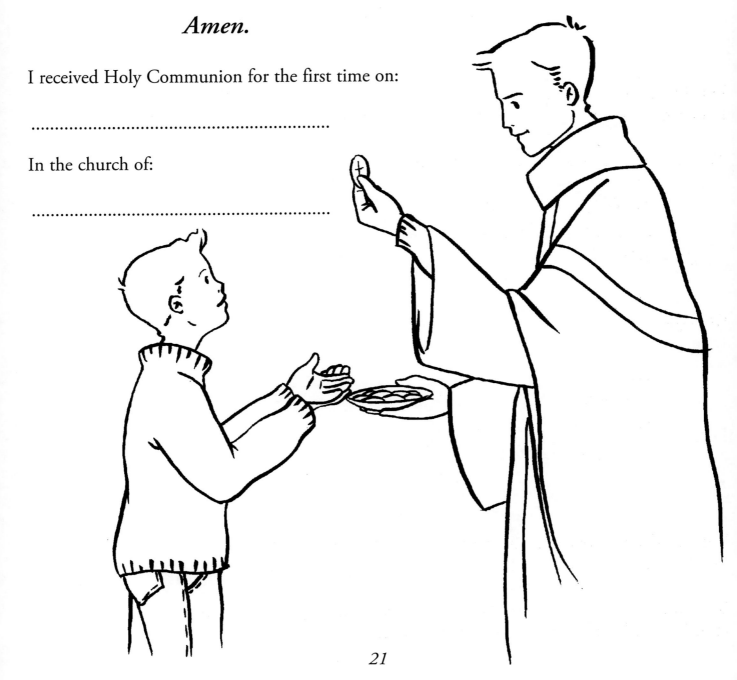

Go in peace.

Thanks be to God!

Lord our God, I thank You for the wonderful gift of Your Son Jesus Christ in Holy Communion.

Lord Jesus, I thank You for living in me. Thank You for Your great love.

Jesus, You send me out to share Your love and Your peace with others.

Jesus,
I want to love others
as You love me.

Lord Jesus, You are always with me.

Jesus,
I remember
Your words
wherever
I am.

Write a prayer to Jesus:

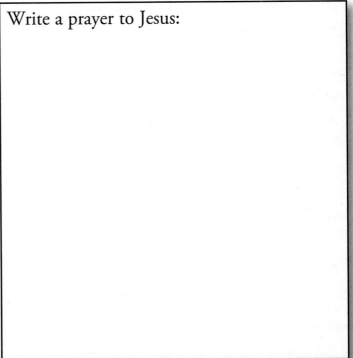

First published in France by
EDITIONS DE L'EMMANUEL
BP 137 – 92 223
Bagneux

English edition first published in United Kingdom in 2000 by
MCCRIMMON PUBLISHING CO. LTD.
10-12 High Street, Great Wakering, Essex, SS3 0EQ

Phone   01702-218956
Email   sales@mccrimmons.com
Web   www.mccrimmons.com

ISBN 978-0-85597-618-7
(Previous ISBN: 0 85597 618 7)

Cum Permissu Superium: Fr. Alain Houry, FEC
                          Visiteur Paris-Rouen
        Nihil Obstat: Fr. George Stokes, Censor Deputatus
        Imprimatur: Mgr. William Nix, Vic. Gen.

Although the publication is free from doctrinal error it does not necessarily reflect the views of those who have granted the Nihil Obstat and Imprimatur

The English translation of the ORDER OF MASS from *The Revised Roman Missal* © 2010, ICEL

Illustrations and cover artwork by Christelle Fargue
Page layout by Brendan Waller
Printed and bound by www.printondemand-worldwide.com